Andrew Brodie ✓

Supporting Maths

FOR AGES 12–13

Contents

Introduction

The *Supporting Maths* series is aimed at all those who work with students who have been identified as needing 'additional' or 'different' support in mathematics. It can be used by anyone working with students who fall into this category, whether you are a teacher, classroom assistant or parent. Notes for non-specialist maths teachers are provided on each worksheet, giving ideas for techniques that can be practised with the students.

Typically, the twelve to thirteen year-old students for whom the book is intended, will be working at the levels expected of primary aged children or they may simply need extra help in tackling the level of work appropriate for Year 8. Their difficulties may be short-term, and overcome with extra practice and support on a one-to-one or small group basis, or they may be long-term, where such support enables them to make progress but at a level behind their peer group.

In this book we provide activities that can be realistically and effectively completed on paper, with the support of an adult. The interaction with the adult gives many opportunities for speaking and listening. Explanation by the adult to the student and by the student to the adult provides a firm foundation for mathematical understanding.

The number work activities in this book use a step-by-step approach. Many Year 8 students are still not confident with multiplication tables so the first eight worksheets feature the tables from two to nine – these include time challenges and, very importantly, links to division questions. We suggest that these worksheets are introduced as 'revision' work to overcome any feelings amongst the students that they are 'too old' to be practising tables. The division work is then extended to cover divisions with remainders, presented as time challenge questions. Students are given revision in the processes of 'short' and 'long' multiplication before tackling questions involving multiplication of decimals. Students are reminded of formal layouts of addition and subtraction questions, including addition and subtraction of decimals, leading to questions involving money and the process of finding change.

By Year 8, students will be familiar with the language of algebra – our worksheets provide revision of this vocabulary as well as practice in the process of dealing with equations and in 'gathering like terms'.

The angles worksheets provide practice in measuring using a protractor and cover the facts that the three angles of a triangle add up to 180°, that angles on a straight line total 180°, that angles around a point total 360° and that angles in a quadrilateral add up to 360°. Further measurement activities include finding areas and perimeters.

Six worksheets relate to handling data and include practice in using the terms mean, median, mode and range as well as work on pie charts and on probability.

Our resource sheets include a mixed range of 'mini facts' that most students will find useful. We suggest that these sheets are photocopied on to card, then laminated and cut into pocket-sized cards. Students can be provided with the appropriate card for use in class lessons.

Students generally achieve the greatest success in an atmosphere of support and encouragement. Praise from a caring adult can be the best reward for the students' efforts. The worksheets and activities in this book will provide many opportunities for students to enjoy these successes. The development of a positive attitude and the resulting increase in self-esteem will help them with all of their schoolwork.

Record and Review

Name: _____ Date of birth: _____

Teacher: _____ Class: _____

Support Assistant: _____

Code of Practice stage: _____ Date targets set: _____

Target

1 _____

2 _____

3 _____

4 _____

Review

Target

1 _____

_____

_____ Target achieved? ⬜ Date _____

2 _____

_____

_____ Target achieved? ⬜ Date _____

3 _____

_____

_____ Target achieved? ⬜ Date _____

4 _____

_____

_____ Target achieved? ⬜ Date _____

The 2 times table and dividing by 2

Name _____

● Write out the two times table as fast as you can.

_____
_____
_____
_____
_____
_____
_____
_____
_____
_____

Use your table to answer these questions. Time yourself using a stopwatch or the second hand on a clock or watch.

$8 \div 2 =$ _____
$16 \div 2 =$ _____
$24 \div 2 =$ _____
$30 \div 2 =$ _____
$12 \div 2 =$ _____
$10 \div 2 =$ _____
$4 \div 2 =$ _____
$14 \div 2 =$ _____
$18 \div 2 =$ _____
$20 \div 2 =$ _____

Time taken

_____

seconds

REVISION REMINDERS

Look: $68 \div 2$ can be written like this $\quad 2\overline{)68}$

Divide the 6 tens first / then divide the 8

$$2\overline{)6^18}^{\ 34}$$

Look: $96 \div 2 = 2\overline{)9^16}^{\ 48}$

Step 1: 9 tens $\div 2 = 4$ tens with a remainder of 1 ten

Step 2: Put the 1 ten with the 6 units to make 16

Step 3: $16 \div 2 = 8$

● Now try these. Work on a separate piece of paper or in an exercise book.

(1) $2\overline{)46}$	(2) $2\overline{)28}$	(3) $2\overline{)84}$	(4) $2\overline{)76}$
(5) $2\overline{)38}$	(6) $2\overline{)70}$	(7) $2\overline{)86}$	(8) $2\overline{)90}$

Notes for teachers

Understandably the students may feel that the two times table is too easy but encourage them to see the activities as a revision exercise. The process of timing adds an extra element of challenge. If the students don't know the table thoroughly, suggest that they practise every day for a week then test them on the sheet again. An improved performance is very motivating. Work through the division example with the students then help them to answer the questions at the bottom of the page.

Andrew Brodie: Supporting Maths 12–13 © A & C Black 2007

The 3 times table and dividing by 3

Name _____

● Write out the three times table as fast as you can.

_____

_____

_____

_____

_____

_____

_____

_____

_____

_____

Use your table to answer these questions. Time yourself using a stopwatch or the second hand on a clock or watch.

$27 \div 3 =$ _____

$9 \div 3 =$ _____

$18 \div 3 =$ _____

$24 \div 3 =$ _____

$12 \div 3 =$ _____

$15 \div 3 =$ _____

$21 \div 3 =$ _____

$6 \div 3 =$ _____

$30 \div 3 =$ _____

$3 \div 3 =$ _____

Time taken

_____

seconds

REVISION REMINDERS

$$\begin{array}{r} 13 \\ 3{\overline{\smash{\big)}\,39}} \end{array}$$

3 tens ÷ 3 = 1 ten ⟋ ⟍ 9 ÷ 3 = 3

$$\begin{array}{r} 1\,4 \\ 4{\overline{\smash{\big)}\,4^1 2}} \end{array}$$

Step 1: 4 tens ÷ 3 = 1 ten with 1 ten left over Step 2: Put the 1 ten with the 2 units to make 12

$$\begin{array}{r} 2\,7 \\ 3{\overline{\smash{\big)}\,8^2 1}} \end{array}$$

Step 1: 8 tens ÷ 3 = 2 tens with 2 tens left over

Step 2: Put the two tens with the 1 unit to make 21

Step 3: 21 ÷ 3 = 7

Step 3: 12 ÷ 3 = 4

● Now try these. Work on a separate piece of paper or in an exercise book.

① $3{\overline{\smash{\big)}\,36}}$ ② $3{\overline{\smash{\big)}\,69}}$ ③ $3{\overline{\smash{\big)}\,99}}$ ④ $3{\overline{\smash{\big)}\,57}}$

⑤ $3{\overline{\smash{\big)}\,72}}$ ⑥ $3{\overline{\smash{\big)}\,51}}$ ⑦ $3{\overline{\smash{\big)}\,51}}$ ⑧ $3{\overline{\smash{\big)}\,126}}$

Notes for teachers

Again the students may feel that the three times table is too easy but encourage them to see the activities as a revision exercise and the process of timing adds an extra element of challenge. If the students do not know the table thoroughly suggest that they practise every day for a week then test them on the sheet again. An improved performance is very motivating. Work through the division example with the students then help them to answer the division questions at the bottom of the page.

The 4 times table and dividing by 4

Name _____

● Write out the four times table as fast as you can.

_____
_____
_____
_____
_____
_____
_____
_____
_____
_____

Use your table to answer these questions. Time yourself using a stopwatch or the second hand on a clock or watch.

$16 \div 4 =$ _____
$12 \div 4 =$ _____
$20 \div 4 =$ _____
$24 \div 4 =$ _____
$8 \div 4 =$ _____
$4 \div 4 =$ _____
$32 \div 4 =$ _____
$40 \div 4 =$ _____
$36 \div 4 =$ _____
$28 \div 4 =$ _____

Time taken

_____

seconds

REVISION REMINDERS

$$4\overline{)48} = 12 \qquad 4\overline{)9^16} = 24 \qquad 4\overline{)7^32} = 18 \qquad 4\overline{)37^12} = 93$$

Step 1: There are not enough hundreds to be divided by 4 so the 3 hundreds are combined with the 7 tens to make 37 tens

Step 2: 37 tens ÷ 4 = 9 tens with 1 ten left over

Step 3: 12 ÷ 4 = 3

● Now try these. Work on a separate piece of paper or in an exercise book.

① $4\overline{)56}$ ② $4\overline{)84}$ ③ $4\overline{)128}$

④ $4\overline{)76}$ ⑤ $4\overline{)92}$ ⑥ $4\overline{)100}$

⑦ $4\overline{)260}$ ⑧ $4\overline{)516}$ ⑨ $4\overline{)956}$

Notes for teachers

Again the students may feel that the four times table is too easy but encourage them to see the activities as a revision exercise. The process of timing adds an extra element of challenge. Watch carefully how they approach the division questions. Work through the division example with the students, then help them to use the same technique with the rest of the questions.

Andrew Brodie: Supporting Maths 12–13 © A & C Black 2007

The 5 times table and dividing by 5

Name _____

● Write out the five times table as fast as you can.

_____

_____

_____

_____

_____

_____

_____

_____

_____

_____

Use your table to answer these questions. Time yourself using a stopwatch or the second hand on a clock or watch.

$25 \div 5 =$ _____

$30 \div 5 =$ _____

$15 \div 5 =$ _____

$20 \div 5 =$ _____

$10 \div 5 =$ _____

$50 \div 5 =$ _____

$5 \div 5 =$ _____

$45 \div 5 =$ _____

$40 \div 5 =$ _____

$35 \div 5 =$ _____

Time taken

_____

seconds

● Try these divisions by 5. Work on a separate piece of paper or in an exercise book.

(1) $5\overline{)125}$ (2) $5\overline{)250}$ (3) $5\overline{)180}$ (4) $5\overline{)365}$

(5) $5\overline{)845}$ (6) $5\overline{)750}$ (7) $5\overline{)75}$ (8) $5\overline{)900}$

(9) Five people share £1000. How much money do they have each?

(10) A circle is cut into 5 equal segments. How big is each angle at the centre?

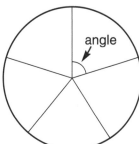
angle

Notes for teachers

For most (though not all) students the five times table is very straightforward but they may still forget which answer goes with which question. Help them to answer the questions and to use the appropriate method to complete the divisions. For question 10, they will need to know that lines that meet at a point make angles totalling 360° around that point so that they will have to divide 360 by 5 to find the answer.

The 6 times table and dividing by 6

Name _____

● Write out your six times table as fast as you can.

_____

_____

_____

_____

_____

_____

_____

_____

_____

_____

Use your table to answer these questions. Time yourself using a stopwatch or the second hand on a clock or watch.

$36 \div 6 =$ _____

$24 \div 6 =$ _____

$30 \div 6 =$ _____

$42 \div 6 =$ _____

$60 \div 6 =$ _____

$6 \div 6 =$ _____

$54 \div 6 =$ _____

$48 \div 6 =$ _____

$12 \div 6 =$ _____

$18 \div 6 =$ _____

Time taken

_____

seconds

● Try these divisions by 6. Work on a separate piece of paper or in an exercise book.

(1) $6\overline{)216}$ (2) $6\overline{)300}$ (3) $6\overline{)486}$ (4) $6\overline{)714}$

(5) $6\overline{)90}$ (6) $6\overline{)900}$ (7) $6\overline{)864}$ (8) $6\overline{)552}$

(9) Six friends share the cost of a meal. The total bill was £84. How much did each person pay?

(10) A car travels 318 miles in 6 hours. What is its average speed in miles per hour?

Notes for teachers

Many students are less confident with the multiplication tables beyond the five times table. Encourage them to learn the six times table and to make use of the table facts to answer the division questions, following the method shown on Worksheets 1–3. Point out that 'average speed' refers to the speed that the car would be travelling at if it could keep up a constant steady speed but that in reality sometimes the car will be going much faster and sometimes much slower.

Andrew Brodie: Supporting Maths 12–13 © A & C Black 2007

The 7 times table and dividing by 7

Name _____

Write out your seven times table as fast as you can.

_____

_____

_____

_____

_____

_____

_____

_____

_____

_____

Use your table to answer these questions. Time yourself using a stopwatch or the second hand on a clock or watch.

$28 \div 7 =$ _____

$14 \div 7 =$ _____

$21 \div 7 =$ _____

$7 \div 7 =$ _____

$35 \div 7 =$ _____

$49 \div 7 =$ _____

$70 \div 7 =$ _____

$63 \div 7 =$ _____

$42 \div 7 =$ _____

$56 \div 7 =$ _____

Time taken

_____

seconds

Try these divisions by 7. Work on a separate piece of paper or in an exercise book.

① $7\overline{)147}$ ② $7\overline{)224}$ ③ $7\overline{)588}$ ④ $7\overline{)903}$

⑤ $7\overline{)91}$ ⑥ $7\overline{)189}$ ⑦ $7\overline{)294}$ ⑧ $7\overline{)385}$

⑨ Seven people have bought equally priced tickets to go to a festival. If the total cost was £203 what did one ticket cost?

⑩ Granny has collected 20p coins in a bottle for many years. She decides to share them equally between her seven grandchildren.

(a) If there are 924 coins in the bottle how many coins does each grandchild get?

(b) What is the value of the coins for each grandchild?

(c) What was the total value of Granny's hoard?

Notes for teachers

Many students are less confident with the multiplication tables beyond the five times table. Encourage them to learn the seven times table and to make use of the tables fact to answer the division questions, following the method shown on Worksheets 1–3. Question 10 parts (b) and (c) may present particular challenges and some students will need help in appreciating that five 20p coins make £1, so dividing the number of coins each grandchild has by 5 will give the value of their share.

The 8 times table and dividing by 8

Name _____

● Write out your eight times table as fast as you can.

_____
_____
_____
_____
_____
_____
_____
_____
_____
_____

Use your table to answer these questions. Time yourself using a stopwatch or the second hand on a clock or watch.

$24 \div 8 =$ _____
$32 \div 8 =$ _____
$16 \div 8 =$ _____
$8 \div 8 =$ _____
$72 \div 8 =$ _____
$80 \div 8 =$ _____
$64 \div 8 =$ _____
$40 \div 8 =$ _____
$52 \div 8 =$ _____
$48 \div 8 =$ _____

Time taken

_____

seconds

● Try these divisions by 8. Work on a separate piece of paper or in an exercise book.

(1) $8\overline{)304}$ (2) $8\overline{)392}$ (3) $8\overline{)3296}$

(4) $8\overline{)2600}$ (5) $8\overline{)4936}$ (6) $8\overline{)6392}$

(7) $8\overline{)1112}$ (8) $8\overline{)2048}$ (9) $8\overline{)2536}$

(10) Eight people did a maths test and were given a score out of 20. Here are the scores:

    14   11   9   15   20   16   14   5

(a) What was the total of all the scores?

(b) What was the mean average score?

Notes for teachers

Many students are less confident with the multiplication tables beyond the five times table. Encourage them to learn the eight times table and to make use of the table facts to answer the division questions, following the method shown on Worksheets 1–3. Question 10 refers to the 'mean average' score. Further work on data handling and the meaning of the word 'mean' is revised on Worksheets 49 and 50. Explain to the students that the **mean** is a type of **average** and can be found by adding all the pieces of data, then dividing by the number of pieces of data.

        Andrew Brodie: Supporting Maths 12–13 © A & C Black 2007

The 9 times table and dividing by 9

Name _____

● Write out your nine times table as fast as you can.

_____
_____
_____
_____
_____
_____
_____
_____
_____
_____

Use your table to answer these questions. Time yourself using a stopwatch or the second hand on a clock or watch.

$72 \div 9 =$ _____
$27 \div 9 =$ _____
$18 \div 9 =$ _____
$36 \div 9 =$ _____
$45 \div 9 =$ _____
$81 \div 9 =$ _____
$90 \div 9 =$ _____
$9 \div 9 =$ _____
$54 \div 9 =$ _____
$63 \div 9 =$ _____

Time taken

_____

seconds

● Try these divisions by 9. Work on a separate piece of paper or in an exercise book.

1. $9{\overline{)243}}$
2. $9{\overline{)774}}$
3. $9{\overline{)1728}}$
4. $9{\overline{)2403}}$
5. $9{\overline{)1485}}$
6. $9{\overline{)5778}}$
7. $9{\overline{)3537}}$
8. $9{\overline{)238473}}$ (It looks big but it works in exactly the same way.)

9. (a) 54 pupils are to be split into 9 equally sized groups. How many pupils are there in each group?

   (b) What would happen if there were 60 pupils? (Discuss this with your teacher.)

Notes for teachers

Most students will be familiar with a range of techniques for remembering the nine times table by, for example, using their fingers or noticing that the digits in each multiple always add up to 9. However, they still need to know the table as thoroughly as possible and ultimately with instant recall. Discuss question 9(b) with the students. What solution can they find?

Division (with remainders) 1

Name _____

● Look at this example:

> The librarian is giving away some old books to 4 pupils. There are 35 books and she wants each pupil to have the same number.
> (a) How many books can each pupil have?
> (b) How many books will be left over?

● Answering the question

Step 1:

There are 4 pupils to share 35 books.

Look at the 4 times table:

$1 \times 4 = 4$
$2 \times 4 = 8$
$3 \times 4 = 12$
$4 \times 4 = 16$
$5 \times 4 = 20$
$6 \times 4 = 24$
$7 \times 4 = 28$
$8 \times 4 = 32$ ← There are enough books to get as far as here.
$9 \times 4 = 36$ ← But not enough books for here.

So we can see that each pupil can have 8 books because $8 \times 4 = 32$ or $4 \times 8 = 32$.

Step 2:

Giving the 4 pupils 8 books each uses 32 books.
As there are 35 books altogether there are 3 left over.

● Now try these questions. Show the remainder if there is one. Work on a separate piece of paper or in an exercise book.

1. $25 \div 4 =$ _____
2. $18 \div 4 =$ _____
3. $36 \div 4 =$ _____
4. $15 \div 4 =$ _____
5. $27 \div 4 =$ _____
6. $33 \div 3 =$ _____
7. $20 \div 4 =$ _____
8. $10 \div 4 =$ _____
9. $5 \div 4 =$ _____
10. $30 \div 4 =$ _____
11. $39 \div 4 =$ _____
12. $54 \div 4 =$ _____

Notes for teachers

For some students the word 'remainder' has little meaning so it is crucial that they understand the example of a realistic situation where the books are being shared out. Some students are likely to respond to the question $35 \div 4$ with the answer '9 remainder 1' because the nearest multiple of 4 to 35 is 36. Discuss why the answer has to be 8 remainder 3 and explain that we always need to look for the multiple below the number being divided.

Division (with remainders) 2

Name _____

How quickly can you answer these questions? Time yourself using a stopwatch or the second hand on a clock or watch.

Column 1	Column 2	Column 3	Column 4
$41 \div 5 =$ _____	$42 \div 5 =$ _____	$33 \div 6 =$ _____	$46 \div 8 =$ _____
$38 \div 9 =$ _____	$51 \div 6 =$ _____	$57 \div 6 =$ _____	$25 \div 7 =$ _____
$50 \div 3 =$ _____	$23 \div 2 =$ _____	$67 \div 4 =$ _____	$46 \div 5 =$ _____
$22 \div 4 =$ _____	$47 \div 5 =$ _____	$43 \div 5 =$ _____	$89 \div 10 =$ _____
$31 \div 4 =$ _____	$23 \div 4 =$ _____	$50 \div 4 =$ _____	$55 \div 4 =$ _____
$29 \div 5 =$ _____	$31 \div 4 =$ _____	$33 \div 5 =$ _____	$32 \div 5 =$ _____
$37 \div 6 =$ _____	$33 \div 2 =$ _____	$47 \div 8 =$ _____	$49 \div 6 =$ _____
$24 \div 5 =$ _____	$28 \div 3 =$ _____	$35 \div 4 =$ _____	$35 \div 2 =$ _____
$37 \div 2 =$ _____	$21 \div 6 =$ _____	$23 \div 3 =$ _____	$67 \div 4 =$ _____
$42 \div 5 =$ _____	$25 \div 4 =$ _____	$36 \div 7 =$ _____	$33 \div 8 =$ _____
$35 \div 4 =$ _____	$45 \div 6 =$ _____	$68 \div 3 =$ _____	$24 \div 5 =$ _____
$29 \div 7 =$ _____	$31 \div 4 =$ _____	$53 \div 4 =$ _____	$37 \div 6 =$ _____
$42 \div 3 =$ _____	$62 \div 5 =$ _____	$22 \div 4 =$ _____	$27 \div 6 =$ _____
$44 \div 5 =$ _____	$73 \div 6 =$ _____	$57 \div 4 =$ _____	$31 \div 5 =$ _____
$38 \div 3 =$ _____	$21 \div 4 =$ _____	$97 \div 5 =$ _____	$29 \div 2 =$ _____

Time taken	Time taken	Time taken	Time taken
_____ seconds	_____ seconds	_____ seconds	_____ seconds

Notes for teachers

This sheet provides excellent practice of multiplication tables as well as further experience of finding remainders. Give appropriate praise when the students complete the first block of questions then encourage them to reach a higher score on the next block. You could repeat this worksheet with them on several occasions with the aim of achieving greater confidence, speed and accuracy.

Multiplication (by units)

Name _____

REVISION REMINDER

We want to multiply 342 by 6:

Start here then work across the number.

```
    3 4 2
x       6
  2 0 5 2
    2  1
```

Step 1: 2 x 6 = 12

Step 2: 4 x 6 = 24 then add 1 to make 25

Step 3: 3 x 6 = 18 then add the 2 to make 20

Now try these. Work on a separate piece of paper or in an exercise book.

(1)
```
  5 9 2
x     7
```

(2)
```
3 6 4 9
x     5
```

(3)
```
2 7 5 6
x     4
```

(4)
```
7 9 6 1
x     2
```

(5)
```
  3 5 4
x     6
```

(6)
```
2 4 3 3
x     5
```

(7)
```
  6 4 7
x     6
```

(8)
```
4 4 6 3
x     7
```

(9)
```
6 5 7 2
x     3
```

(10) A computer game costs £34.96.

What would 8 of these games cost altogether?

Clue: it's easier to take out the decimal point and multiply 3496 x 8, then put the decimal point in the correct place in the answer.

Notes for teachers

The students will have been introduced to a variety of methods for multiplication in the primary school and many will be familiar with the grid method. This worksheet focuses on a more traditional method – many students will have been shown this by their parents and may have become confused by the contrasting approaches. By studying the example with them you may be able to overcome their confusion while at the same time providing them with a method that is quick and efficient.

Multiplication (by tens)

Name _____

REVISION REMINDER

Look: we want to multiply 359 by 70.

```
    3 5 9
x    7 0
---------
2 5 1 3 0
    4 6
```

Step 1: First write a zero in the units column then start here

Step 2: 9 x 7 = 63 so write the 3 then give the 6 to the next column

Step 3: 5 x 7 = 35, then add the 6 to get 41

Step 4: 3 x 7 = 21 then add 4 to make 25

⬤ Try these. Work on a separate piece of paper or in an exercise book.

①
```
  2 3 4
x    4 0
```

②
```
  4 1 6
x    3 0
```

③
```
5 1 9 2
x    6 0
```

④
```
  3 5 4
x    2 0
```

⑤
```
8 5 6 7
x    3 0
```

⑥
```
  3 5 2
x    4 0
```

⑦
```
4 2 1 5
x    5 0
```

⑧
```
6 4 4 7
x    2 0
```

⑨
```
2 3 9 0
x    4 0
```

⑩ 60 people each pay £249 to go on a flight to Egypt.
What is the total amount spent?

Notes for teachers

This worksheet continues the process of introducing a method of multiplication that is quick and efficient and follows a clear set of rules.

Multiplication (by tens and units)

Name _____

REVISION REMINDER

Look: we want to multiply 398 x 42.

```
    3 9 8
x     4 2
─────────
    7 9 6
+ 1 5 9 2 0
─────────
  1 6 7 1 6
```

Step 1: Multiply by the 2 units and write the answer here

Step 2: Put a 0, then multiply by the 4 tens

Step 3: Add the two answers and write the result here

⬤ Try these. Work on a separate piece of paper or in an exercise book.

(1)
```
    4 6 7
x     3 4
```

(2)
```
    5 3 6
x     6 7
```

(3)
```
    2 3 7
x     5 8
```

(4)
```
    7 8 2
x     2 1
```

(5)
```
    3 8 4
x     8 9
```

(6)
```
    6 7 3
x     9 2
```

(7)
```
    8 3 7
x     3 3
```

(8)
```
    3 7 2
x     1 9
```

(9)
```
    2 2 5
x     4 5
```

(10) 34 boxes each contain 267 nails.
How many nails are there altogether?

Notes for teachers

This worksheet follows on from Worksheets 11 and 12 and introduces long multiplication by tens and units. Help the students to analyse the example encouraging them to observe that the first line of the answer has been reached through multiplying by units, that the second line results from multiplying by tens and the final answer is achieved by combining the other two answers.

Andrew Brodie: Supporting Maths 12–13 © A & C Black 2007

Multiplying decimals (Discussion sheet)

Name _____

⬤ Estimate the answer to this question:

3.4 x 1.6 _____

⬤ Now try the question on a calculator.

Write down the answer you find: _____

⬤ Now look at a way of finding the answer without the calculator.

Step 1: Write the question without the decimal points:

34 x 16

Step 2: Multiply

… then add the answers.

$$
\begin{array}{r}
3\,4 \\
\times\ \ 1\,6 \\
\hline
2\,0\,4 \\
+\ 3\,4\,0 \\
\hline
5\,4\,5 \\
\end{array}
$$

← 34 x 6 goes here

← 34 x 10 goes here

Step 3: Look back at the original question and count the decimal places.

3.4 x 1.6

1 decimal place ↗   ↖ 1 decimal place

There are 2 decimal places in the question.

Step 4. So there must be 2 decimal places in the answer.

5.44

two decimal places

Notes for teachers

If the students have been successful with Worksheet 13 they are able to move on to multiplying decimals together. Encourage them to make a reasonable estimate. They could round the two numbers to the nearest whole number: 3.4 can be rounded to 3 and 1.6 can be rounded to 2. 3 x 2 = 6 so the answer 3.4 x 1.6 will be reasonably close to 6. Ensure that they read the calculator display correctly. Now help them work through the example.

Multiplying decimals

Name _____

● Look at this question: 1.25 x 7.3

REVISION REMINDER

Step 1:   Write the question without the decimal points   125 x 73

Step 2:   Multiply

```
    1 2 5
  x  7 3
  -------
    3 7 5
  8 7 5 0
  -------
  9 1 2 5
```

Step 3: Count the decimal places in 1.25 x 7.3

Step 4: So there must be three decimal places in the answer: 9.125

● Try these. Work on a separate piece of paper or in an exercise book.

(1) 0.6 x 0.4	(2) 5.7 x 3.2	(3) 2.8 x 0.7
(4) 0.8 x 0.2	(5) 7.9 x 0.4	(6) 12.6 x 1.7
(7) 14.3 x 2.9	(8) 28.1 x 0.6	(9) 3.75 x 4

● Now try this:

(10) Apples are for sale at a price of £1.12 per kilogram. Sidney buys four and a half kilograms of the apples. What is the total price he pays?

Notes for teachers

Help the students analyse the example before attempting the questions. For question 10 they may need reminding that 'four and a half' can be written as 4.5.

   Andrew Brodie: Supporting Maths 12–13 © A & C Black 2007

Addition of large numbers

Name _____

⬤ Look at this addition: 27342 + 4628 + 219

Step 1: Write it in columns.

Make sure that the units are all in line.

```
  2 7 3 4 2
+   4 6 2 8
      2 1 9
```

The 2, 8 and 9 are all in the units column.

Step 2: Start adding at the right-hand side, the work across the question adding each column in turn.

```
  2 7 3 4 2
+   4 6 2 8
      2 1 9
  3 2 1 8 9
  1 1   1
```

Keep these very small.

⬤ Try these additions. Work on a separate piece of paper or in an exercise book. Work tidily but as quickly as possible.

(1) 3217 + 496

(2) 16642 + 7167

(3) 46318 + 27399

(4) 72845 + 7285

(5) 13747 + 892 + 1467 + 11615

(6) Dave retires and decides to buy a new car priced £12995 and a caravan priced £9995. What do they cost altogether?

Notes for teachers

Many students make mistakes with addition and subtraction simply because they do not enter the numbers correctly in the columns – tidiness is crucial. Work through the example very carefully with them, ensuring that they read and understand the accompanying notes, then help them to complete the questions.

Addition of decimals

Name _____

● Look at this addition: $17 + 2.6 + 4.37$

Step 1: Write it in columns.

Make sure that the units are all in line.

```
   17
    2.6
+   4.37
_____
```

The 7, 2 and 4 are all in the units column.

Step 2: Start adding at the right-hand side, the work across the question adding each column in turn. Don't forget to show the decimal point in your answer.

```
   17
    2.6
+   4.37
_____
   23.97
     1
```

● Try these additions. Work on a separate piece of paper or in an exercise book. Work tidily but as quickly as possible.

① $42.7 + 3.8$

② $7 + 6.9 + 4 + 13.24$

③ $168 + 29.4$

④ $217 + 38.7 + 116$

⑤ $92.4 + 11 + 6.73$

⑥ $58 + 9.92 + 8.16$

⑦

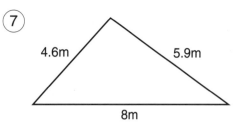

4.6m   5.9m

8m

Find the perimeter of this triangle.

Notes for teachers

These questions require looking at the tenths and hundredths columns and their positions relative to the units. Encourage the students to follow the rules that 'you always keep the units in line' or 'you always keep the decimal points in line'. Again, tidiness is crucial. Some students find it helpful to put decimal points and extra noughts to make all the columns neat.

 Andrew Brodie: Supporting Maths 12–13 © A & C Black 2007

Subtraction of large numbers

Name _____

● 30000 – 13495

Step 1: Write it in columns.

```
  3 0 0 0 0
– 1 3 4 9 5
_____
```

Step 2: Split

First use one from the ten thousands column to make 10 thousands.

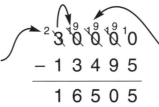

Look we are using 1 from each column to give 10 to the next column, then when we use 1 from that column we leave 9 behind.

```
2  9 9 9 1
  3 0 0 0 0
– 1 3 4 9 5
_____
  1 6 5 0 5
```

2 – 1 = 1
9 – 3 = 6
9 – 4 = 5
9 – 9 = 0
10 – 5 = 5

● Try these. Work on a separate piece of paper or in an exercise book.

①
```
  4 0 0 0 0
– 2 3 4 9 6
```

②
```
  3 0 0 0
– 1 6 9 9
```

③
```
  4 0 0 6
– 1 2 1 1
```

④
```
  7 1 0 4
– 2 9 8 6
```

Hint: you don't need any extra units to do this column.

⑤
```
  1 3 0 0 0
–   5 6 4 8
```

⑥
```
  2 0 0 0 0
–   7 3 0 9
```

⑦
```
  1 7 1 2 3
–   8 4 6 5
```

⑧
```
  1 0 0 0 0 0
–           1
```

⑨ Sid gets paid £1000 and decides to buy a camera for £465.
How much money will he have left?

Notes for teachers

Many students make mistakes with addition and subtraction simply because they do not enter the numbers correctly in the columns – tidiness is crucial. Work through the example very carefully with the students, ensuring that they read and understand the accompanying notes. Ensure that they understand that the five units can only be subtracted if extra units are created from a ten; however, there are no tens available so some need to be created from a hundred; there are no hundreds so some need to be created from a thousand but there are no thousands so some need to be created from a ten thousand. Once a ten thousand is broken into ten thousands, one of these can be broken into ten hundreds, one of these can be broken into ten tens and one of these into ten units. The question then becomes extremely easy.

Subtraction of decimals (Discussion sheet)

Name _____

● Look: 6 cakes

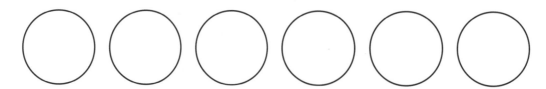

● Look at this diagram where each of the cakes has been cut into 10 equal pieces.

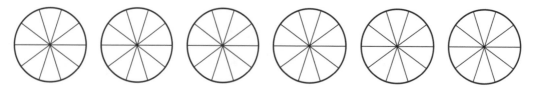

● Now look at this question: 6 − 4.2 =

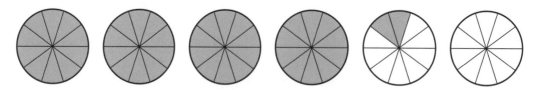

You can see that 4.2 cakes are shaded and 1.8 cakes are unshaded…
… so 6 − 4.2 = 1.8

● Look at the question on a number line.

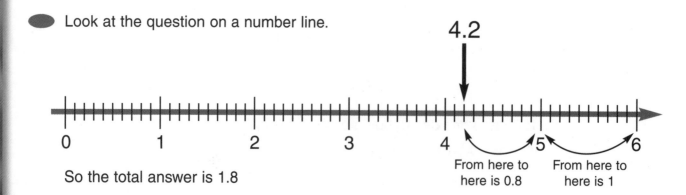

4.2

0   1   2   3   4   5   6

From here to here is 0.8   From here to here is 1

So the total answer is 1.8

Notes for teachers

Help the students to read through the examples. Ensure that they understand that the cakes are each cut into ten equal pieces, that each of these pieces is therefore one tenth of a cake and that one tenth can be shown as 0.1 i.e. 0 in the units column and 1 in the tenths column. Do they recognise the picture as representing 6 cakes with 4.2 cakes shaded? Do they see how this is represented on the number line?

Subtraction of decimals

Name _____

● Use the number line to help answer these questions.

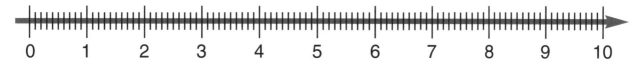

0 1 2 3 4 5 6 7 8 9 10

1. 6 − 4.2 =

2. 8 − 2.7 =

3. 3 − 1.4 =

4. 10 − 5.8 =

5. 9 − 5.4 =

6. 7 − 3.9 =

● Look at a different way to subtract decimals:

$$
\begin{array}{r} 6 \\ -\ 4.2 \\ \hline \end{array}
\qquad
\begin{array}{r} 6.0 \\ -\ 4.2 \\ \hline \end{array}
\qquad
\begin{array}{r} {}^{5}\!\!\not{6}.{}^{1}0 \\ -\ 4.2 \\ \hline 1.8 \end{array}
$$

The units are lined up

● Try these:

1.
$$
\begin{array}{r} 8 \\ -\ 3.5 \\ \hline \end{array}
$$

2.
$$
\begin{array}{r} 6 \\ -\ 2.4 \\ \hline \end{array}
$$

3.
$$
\begin{array}{r} 4 \\ -\ 1.9 \\ \hline \end{array}
$$

4.
$$
\begin{array}{r} 7 \\ -\ 2.5 \\ \hline \end{array}
$$

● Now try these:

5.
$$
\begin{array}{r} 4.1 \\ -\ 2.9 \\ \hline \end{array}
$$

6.
$$
\begin{array}{r} 3.2 \\ -\ 1.7 \\ \hline \end{array}
$$

7.
$$
\begin{array}{r} 9.4 \\ -\ 5.9 \\ \hline \end{array}
$$

8.
$$
\begin{array}{r} 8.3 \\ -\ 5.7 \\ \hline \end{array}
$$

Notes for teachers

This worksheet should be completed after you have discussed the examples on Worksheet 19. Help the students work through the questions, ensuring that they lay them out correctly and follow the appropriate method.

Money
(change from £5)

Name _____

● I spend £3.46

Here is one way to find my change from £5:

$$
\begin{array}{r}
{}^4\!\not5.{}^9\!\not0\,{}^1\!0 \\
-\quad 3.46 \\
\hline
1.54
\end{array}
$$ So the change is £1.54.

● Now try these:

① $\begin{array}{r} 5.00 \\ -\ 1.72 \\ \hline \\ \hline \end{array}$ ② $\begin{array}{r} 5.00 \\ -\ 2.98 \\ \hline \\ \hline \end{array}$ ③ $\begin{array}{r} 5.00 \\ -\ 3.67 \\ \hline \\ \hline \end{array}$ ④ $\begin{array}{r} 5.00 \\ -\ 2.13 \\ \hline \\ \hline \end{array}$

⑤ I buy a notebook for £1.65 and a pen for 95p.

    (i)   How much do I spend altogether?   _____

    (ii) What is my change from £5?   _____

⑥ I buy a hot chocolate for £1.35 and a muffin for £1.49.

    (i)   How much do I spend altogether?   _____

    (ii) What is my change from £5?   _____

Notes for teachers

On this worksheet the students are encouraged to use the 'decomposition' method for subtraction when finding change from £5. You may also like to remind them of the 'counting on' method, traditionally used by shopkeepers – a number line is helpful for this. Discuss the example with them before helping them to tackle the questions. Note that questions 5 and 6 require the students to add total bills before finding change.

 Andrew Brodie: Supporting Maths 12–13 © A & C Black 200

Money
(change from £10)

Name _____

● I spend £2.84

Here is one way to find my change from £10:

$$\begin{array}{r} {}^{0}\cancel{1}{}^{9}\cancel{0}.{}^{9}\cancel{0}{}^{1}0 \\ -\quad 2.84 \\ \hline 7.16 \end{array}$$ So the change is £7.16

● Try these:

(1)　　10.00
　　－　4.49
　　_____

　　_____

(2)　　10.00
　　－　6.35
　　_____

　　_____

(3)　　10.00
　　－　1.98
　　_____

　　_____

(4)　　10.00
　　－　8.99
　　_____

　　_____

(5)　I buy three cups of coffee costing £1.65 each.

　(i)　How much do I spend altogether?　　_____

　(ii)　What is my change from £10?　　_____

(6)　I download ten songs to my ipod. Each song costs 79p.

　(i)　How much do I spend altogether?　　_____

　(ii)　If I had exactly £10 before I bought
　　the songs, how much have I got left?　　_____

Notes for teachers

On this worksheet the students are encouraged to use the 'decomposition' method for subtraction when finding change from £10. You may also like to remind them of the 'counting on' method, traditionally used by shopkeepers – a number line is helpful for this. Discuss the example with them before helping them to tackle the questions. Note that questions 5 and 6 require the students to find total bills using multiplication before finding change.

Money
(change from £100)

Name _____

● I spend £78.34

Here is one way to find my change from £100:

$$\begin{array}{r} {}^0\!{}^1\!1\,{}^9\!0\,{}^9\!0\,.\,{}^9\!0\,{}^1\!0 \\ -\ 78.34 \\ \hline 21.66 \end{array}$$ So the change is £21.66

● Try these:

①
$$\begin{array}{r} 100.00 \\ -\ 14.67 \\ \hline \\ \hline \end{array}$$

②
$$\begin{array}{r} 100.00 \\ -\ 84.92 \\ \hline \\ \hline \end{array}$$

③
$$\begin{array}{r} 100.00 \\ -\ 49.99 \\ \hline \\ \hline \end{array}$$

④ I buy 4 packs of coloured printer paper for £6.99 each and 2 inkjet cartridges costing £12.98 each.

(a) What do I pay for the paper? _____

(b) What do I pay for the cartridges? _____

(c) How much do I spend altogether? _____

(d) What is my change from £100? _____

Notes for teachers

On this worksheet the students are encouraged to use the 'decomposition' method for subtraction when finding change from £100. You may also like to remind them of the 'counting on' method, traditionally used by shopkeepers – a number line is helpful for this. Discuss the example with them before helping them to tackle the questions. Some students may need particular help with question 4 where each part must be completed before finding the final answer.

Algebra
(Discussion sheet)

Name _____

- Look : $6 + 2 = 3 + 5$

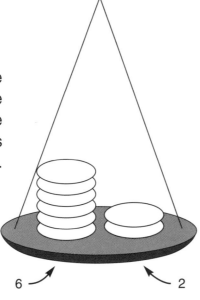

The scales are balanced because there is the same amount on both sides of the equation.

6 ⟶   2 ⟵   3 ⟶   5 ⟵

Look at this equation where x represents a mystery number:

$$x + 3 = 7$$

You can probably see straight away that the x is worth 4 because $4 + 3 = 7$

But here is another way to consider the question.

$x + 3 = 7$ is a balanced equation

We want the x on its own so we need to take the 3 away. To keep the equation balanced we need to take 3 away from the other side as well:

So $x = 4$

This side is just x because we have taken the 3 away.

This side is 4 because, to be fair, we took 3 away from 7 as well.

Notes for teachers

Discuss the illustration with the students, establishing the rule that every equation is balanced and that whatever is done to one side of an equation must be done to the other side. Show them how this method is used to isolate the mystery letter (in this case x) so that its value can be found.

Algebra (subtracting from both sides of an equation)

Name _____

● In each equation below, find the value of x by taking away the same amount from both sides.

① $x + 2 = 9$

$x =$ _____

② $x + 6 = 15$

$x =$ _____

③ $x + 7 = 20$

$x =$ _____

④ $x + 20 = 100$

$x =$ _____

⑤ $x + 17 = 30$

$x =$ _____

⑥ $x + 3 = 7$

$x =$ _____

⑦ $x + 5 = 12$

$x =$ _____

⑧ $x + 4 = 13$

$x =$ _____

⑨ $x + 1 = 8$

$x =$ _____

● Sometimes the x is the other side.

Look: $6 = x + 2$

Swap sides: $x + 2 = 6$

Subtract 2 from both sides: $x = 4$

● Try these:

⑩ $7 = x + 5$

= _____

= _____

⑪ $10 = x + 3$

= _____

= _____

⑫ $8 = x + 7$

= _____

= _____

● Sometimes the value of x will be a negative number.

Look: $x + 3 = 1$

$x = 1 - 3$ ⟩ Subtract 3 from both sides.

$x = -2$

● Try these:

⑬ $x + 4 = 3$

$x =$ _____

$x =$ _____

⑭ $x + 7 = 5$

$x =$ _____

$x =$ _____

⑮ $x + 1 = 0$

$x =$ _____

$x =$ _____

Notes for teachers

This worksheet follows on from Worksheet 24 using the rule that every equation is balanced and that whatever is done to one side of an equation must be done to the other side. This method is used to isolate the mystery letter so that its value can be found. Help the students to see why a particular number is subtracted e.g. in question 1 we subtract 2 from both sides.

Andrew Brodie: Supporting Maths 12–13 © A & C Black 2007

Algebra (adding to both sides of an equation)

Name _____

● Look:

$$x - 2 = 5$$

You can probably see straight away that x is worth 7 because

$$7 - 2 = 5$$

But here is another way to consider the question

$x - 2 = 5$ is a balanced equation.

We want the x on its own so we need to add 2 to cancel out the −2. To keep the equation balanced we need to add 2 to the other side as well.

So $x = 7$

This side is just x because we have added 2 to the −2 to make 0.

This side is 7 because, to be fair, we added 2 to 5 as well.

● In each equation below, find the value of x by adding the same amount to both sides.

1. $x - 4 = 6$

   $x = $ _____

2. $x - 3 = 2$

   $x = $ _____

3. $x - 4 = 12$

   $x = $ _____

4. $x - 3 = 9$

   $x = $ _____

5. $x - 8 = 15$

   $x = $ _____

6. $x - 6 = 14$

   $x = $ _____

7. $x - 18 = 12$

   $x = $ _____

8. $x - 9 = 21$

   $x = $ _____

9. $x - 25 = 75$

   $x = $ _____

Notes for teachers

This worksheet follows on from Worksheet 24 using the rule that every equation is balanced and that whatever is done to one side of an equation must be done to the other side. This method is used to isolate the mystery letter so that its value can be found. Help the students to see why a particular number is added.

Algebra (dividing both sides of an equation)

Name _____

● Look:

$2x = 8$

Don't forget that this means $2 \times x$

If $2x = 8$

$x = 4$ (because 2 x 4 = 8)

● Here is another way to consider the question:

$2x = 8$ is a balanced equation.

We want the x on its own so we need to *divide* by 2 to cancel out the multiplication by 2. To keep the equation balanced we need to divide the other side by 2 as well.

$2x = 8$

so $x = 4$

This side is just x because we have divided by 2 to cancel out the multiplication by 2.

This side is 4 because, to be fair, we divided 8 by 2 as well.

● In each equation below, find the value of x by dividing both sides by the same amount.

① $2x = 6$

$x =$ _____

② $4x = 16$

$x =$ _____

③ $5x = 20$

$x =$ _____

④ $3x = 15$

$x =$ _____

⑤ $6x = 12$

$x =$ _____

⑥ $5x = 45$

$x =$ _____

⑦ $2x = 36$

$x =$ _____

⑧ $4x = 24$

$x =$ _____

Notes for teachers

This worksheet follows on from Worksheet 24 using the rule that every equation is balanced and that whatever is done to one side of an equation must be done to the other side. This method is used to isolate the mystery letter so that its value can be found. Help the students to see why both sides of each equation are being divided by a particular number.

Andrew Brodie: Supporting Maths 12–13 © A & C Black 2007

Algebra (gathering like terms) 1

Name _____

● Sometimes you don't need to find the values of mystery letters but you might be asked to gather them together. We call this process 'gathering like terms'.

Look:

$$3y + 2y$$

3y means 3 x y which is the same as $y + y + y$

2y means 2 x y which is the same as $y + y$

...so $3y + 2y$ is equal to $5y$.

This is a way of simplifying the expression.

Here is another example:

$$4b + 5b$$

$$4b + 5b = 9b$$

And another…

$$7d - 3d = 4d$$

● Try simplifying these expressions by gathering like terms:

1	$4z + 2z =$ _____	2	$9y + 3y =$ _____
3	$3x + x =$ _____	4	$8w - 3w =$ _____
5	$2v + 6v =$ _____	6	$10u - 4u =$ _____
7	$5t + 4t + 2t =$ _____	8	$3s + 7s + s =$ _____
9	$6r + 3r - 2r =$ _____	10	$4q - q + 3q =$ _____

Notes for teachers

Students are sometimes surprised that they do not need to find an 'answer' to a question. In the questions on this worksheet the students need to 'gather like terms'. Remind the students that x is the same as $1x$ but we simply don't bother to write the 1.

Algebra (gathering like terms together) 2

Name _____

● Look at this expression:

$$3x + 2x + 2y$$

This is a y term.

This is called an x term.

This is an x term.

When you simplify expressions you can only gather together terms that are like each other. That is why we call this process 'gathering like terms'.

So, to simplify the example above we get:

$$3x + 2x + 2y = 5x + 2y$$

These are like each other because they are both x terms. They are called 'like terms'.

The like terms have been gathered together.

Nothing has happened to the y term.

Here is another example: Simplify $4a + 3a + 3b + 5b$

$$4a + 3a + 3b + 5b = 7a + 8b$$

● Simplify the following equations:

① $5x + 2y + 3x =$ _____

② $6a + 2b + 3b + a =$ _____

③ $3c + 2d - 2c + d =$ _____
(Clue: $3c - 2c = 1c$ but we just write c instead of $1c$.)

④ $4s + 3s + 6 =$ _____
(Clue: the 6 is not like the other two terms so will stay as it is.)

⑤ $3j + 2k - j - k =$ _____

⑥ $5f + 3f + 4 - 2f =$ _____

⑦ $9g - 5 - 6g =$ _____

⑧ $2m + 4 + 7 + 3m =$ _____

⑨ $5n - 3 - 2 + 2n =$ _____

Notes for teachers

Help the students to gather like terms. Help them to realise that x terms cannot be mixed with y terms, etc. Watch carefully how they tackle each question, ensuring that they read the clues provided.

Andrew Brodie: Supporting Maths 12–13 © A & C Black 2007

Measuring acute angles

Name _____

● This is a right angle.

A right angle has 90°.

This is the symbol for a right angle.

● This is an acute angle.

An acute angle is smaller than 90°.

● Estimate the size of each angle then measure it.

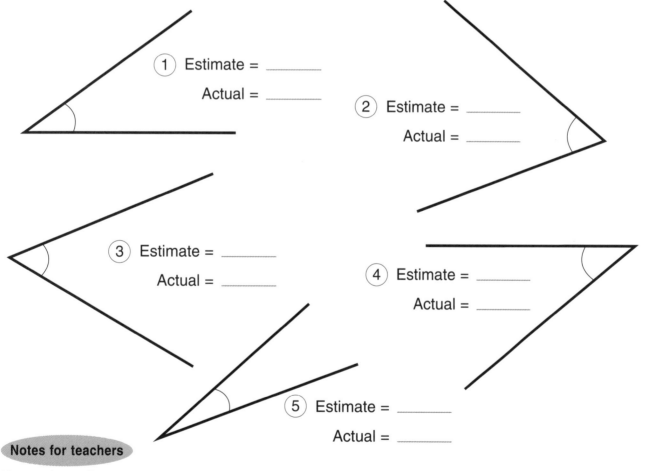

(1) Estimate = _____

Actual = _____

(2) Estimate = _____

Actual = _____

(3) Estimate = _____

Actual = _____

(4) Estimate = _____

Actual = _____

(5) Estimate = _____

Actual = _____

Notes for teachers

Most students will possess a protractor in their pencil case but many will not be sure how to use it. Help them to identify the key points on the protractor: the cross that needs to be aligned with the 'point' of the angle, the zero for the outer ring of numbers and the zero for the inner ring of numbers. Help them to align one of the zero lines with one of the lines of the angle then to read the correct size e.g. if they have aligned the zero from the outer ring they need to read the size from the outer ring. Estimating the angle size before measuring it prompts the students to look again at their answer if the result is surprising. Odd results are usually caused through looking at the outer ring instead of the inner ring or vice versa.

Measuring obtuse angles

Name _____

● This is a right angle.
 A right angle has 90°.

● This is an obtuse angle.
 An obtuse angle is bigger than 90°.

● Estimate the size of each angle then measure it.

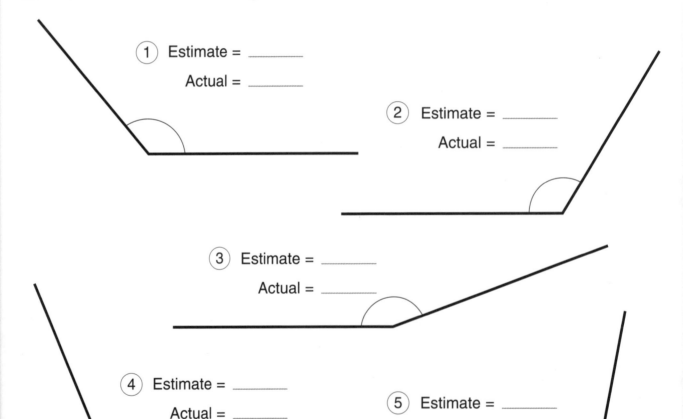

(1) Estimate = _____

 Actual = _____

(2) Estimate = _____

 Actual = _____

(3) Estimate = _____

 Actual = _____

(4) Estimate = _____

 Actual = _____

(5) Estimate = _____

 Actual = _____

Notes for teachers

Most students will possess a protractor in their pencil case but many will not be sure how to use it. Help them to identify the key points on the protractor: the cross that needs to be aligned with the 'point' of the angle, the zero for the outer ring of numbers and the zero for the inner ring of numbers. Help them to align one of the zero lines with one of the lines of the angle then to read the correct size e.g. if they have aligned the zero from the outer ring they need to read the size from the outer ring. Estimating the angle size before measuring it prompts the students to look again at their answer if the result is surprising. Odd results are usually caused through looking at the outer ring instead of the inner ring or vice versa.

 Andrew Brodie: Supporting Maths 12–13 © A & C Black 2007

Measuring reflex angles

Name _____

● Look:

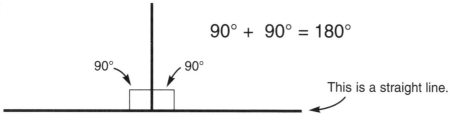

$90° + 90° = 180°$

90°   90°

This is a straight line.

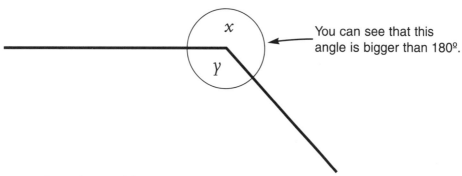

x

y

You can see that this angle is bigger than 180°.

Angle x and angle y add up to 360°.

To find the size of angle x, measure angle y then subtract this size from 360°.

Use your protractor to measure $\angle y$. $\angle y =$ _____

Now subtract: 360

− _____

$\angle x =$ _____

● Try this one:

Find the size of $\angle a$

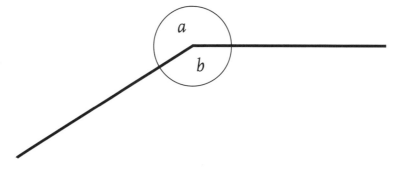

a

b

Notes for teachers

Explain to the students that the reflex angle can be found by first measuring the smaller angle then subtracting from 360°. Again, encourage them to estimate first to see if their measured result is reasonable.

Angles (on a straight line 1)

Name _____

⬤ Look:

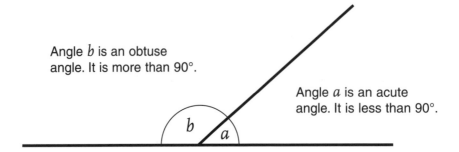

Angle b is an obtuse angle. It is more than 90°.

Angle a is an acute angle. It is less than 90°.

b a

Use a protractor. Measure angle a. $\angle\, a =$ _____

This symbol is used instead of writing the word 'angle.'

Now measure angle b. $\angle\, b =$ _____

We still use this symbol even though the angle is obtuse.

Add together the two sizes: $a + b =$ _____

This should come to 180°. If it's not exactly 180°, that's because the angles are difficult to measure accurately.

Angles on a straight line always add up to 180°.

Notes for teachers

This worksheet is designed to encourage students to understand that angles on a straight line add up to 180°. Measuring may not produce this result, however, because accuracy is extremely difficult with a protractor and the students may need to be convinced that it's true!

   Andrew Brodie: Supporting Maths 12–13 © A & C Black 2007

Angles (on a straight line 2)

Name _____

⬤ Look:

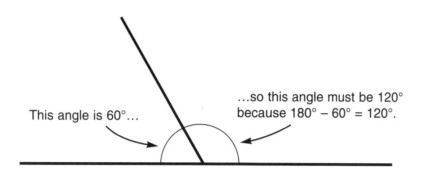

This angle is 60°...

...so this angle must be 120° because 180° − 60° = 120°.

Angles on a straight line always add up to 180°.

⬤ Find the sizes of the missing angles.

①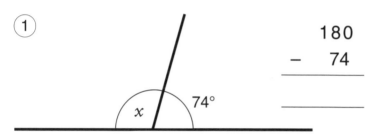

74°

```
  180
−  74
──────
```

∠ x = _____

(Don't forget the degrees sign °)

②

123°

y

∠ y = _____

③

∠ w = _____

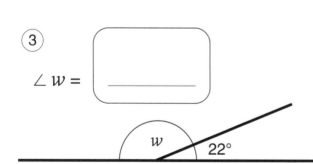

w

22°

④

46°   z

∠ z = _____

Notes for teachers

Remind the students of the fact that the angles on a straight line add up to 180° then help them to complete the questions. Ensure that they always remember the degrees symbol in their answers.

Angles
(around a point)

Name _____

● Look:

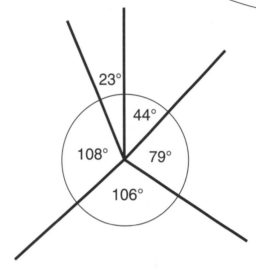

Add the angles together.

```
      1 0 8
      1 0 6
        7 9
        4 4
  +     2 3
  _____

  _____
```

You should have found that the angles add up to 360°. Angles around a point always add up to 360°.

● Find the size of the missing angle by adding the others together then subtracting from 360°.

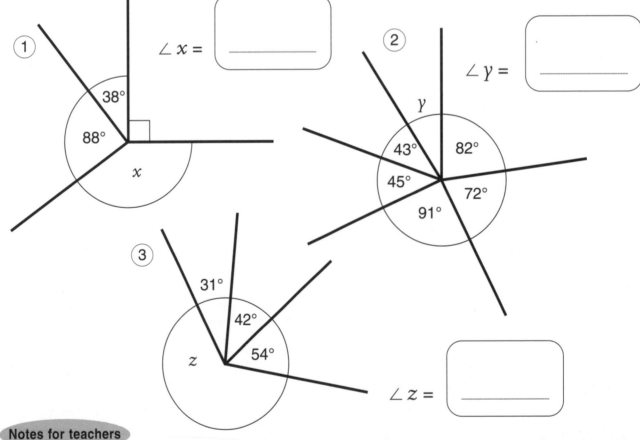

① ∠x = _____

② ∠y = _____

③ ∠z = _____

Notes for teachers

This worksheet is designed to encourage students to understand that angles around a point add up to 360°. Measuring may not produce this result, however, because accuracy is extremely difficult with a protractor. With the three questions, ensure that the students add the angles correctly before they subtract the total from 360° to find the missing angle.

Angles in a triangle

Name _____

⬤ Measure the size of each angle.

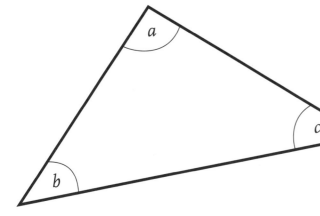

∠ a = _____

∠ b = _____

∠ c = _____

∠ a + ∠ b + ∠ c = _____

This should come to 180°. If it's not
exactly 180° that's because the angles
are difficult to measure accurately.

⬤ The three angles of a triangle always add up to 180°. If we know two of the angles
we can find the third. Find the missing angles in each of these two triangles.

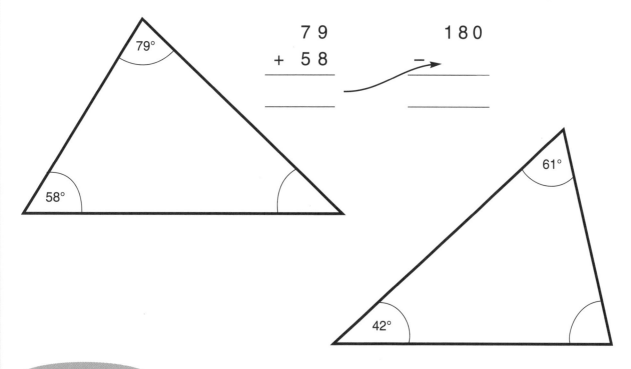

$$\begin{array}{r} 7\ 9 \\ +\ \ 5\ 8 \\ \hline \end{array}$$

$$\begin{array}{r} 1\ 8\ 0 \\ - \\ \hline \end{array}$$

Notes for teachers

Watch carefully how the students use the protractor. Make sure that they align one of the protractor's zero lines with one
line of the angle they are measuring and that they then read the size from either the outer or inner ring of the protractor's
scale, depending on whether they used the outer or inner zero. Once again, students may not find that their three
measured angles add up to 180° simply because accuracy is not easy with a protractor.

Quadrilaterals (Discussion sheet)

Name _____

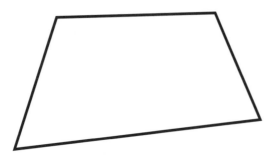

This shape has four sides. It is a quadrilateral. The prefix 'quad' means 4.

These shapes are all special quadrilaterals:

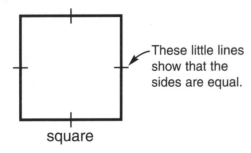

These little lines show that the sides are equal.

square

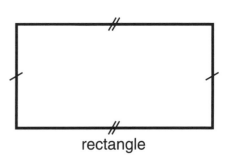

rectangle

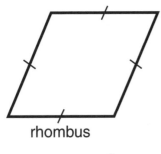

A rhombus has 4 equal sides. It's like a square that's been pushed over.

rhombus

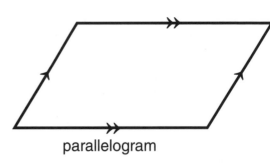

parallelogram

A parallelogram is like a rectangle that's been pushed over. It has opposite sides that are parallel.

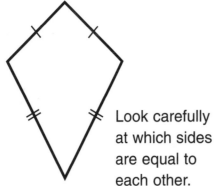

Look carefully at which sides are equal to each other.

kite

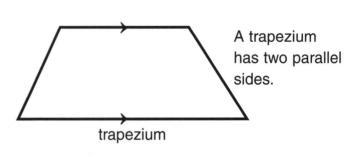

A trapezium has two parallel sides.

trapezium

Notes for teachers

Discuss each of the shapes in turn, pointing out the markings that show which sides are equal or which sides are parallel. Discuss the fact that some of the shapes could have extra markings. The square could have parallel arrows to show that its opposite sides are parallel but we don't bother with them because we accept that they are parallel. Encourage the students to look carefully at the trapezium. A trapezium always has one pair of parallel sides but the other sides can be at different angles from the one in the picture.

Andrew Brodie: Supporting Maths 12–13 © A & C Black 2007

Angles in a quadrilateral

Name _____

⬤ Measure the size of each angle.

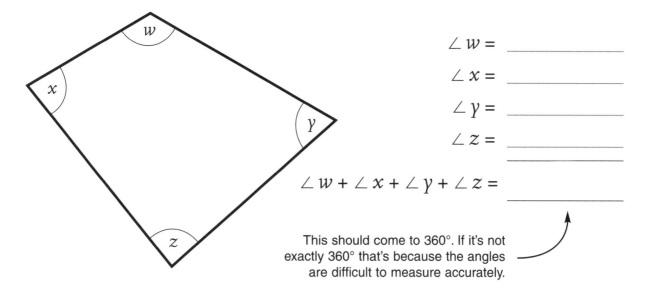

$\angle w =$ _____

$\angle x =$ _____

$\angle y =$ _____

$\angle z =$ _____

$\angle w + \angle x + \angle y + \angle z =$ _____

This should come to 360°. If it's not exactly 360° that's because the angles are difficult to measure accurately.

⬤ The four angles of a quadrilateral always add up to 360°. If we know three of the angles, we can find the fourth. Find the missing angles in each of these quadrilaterals.

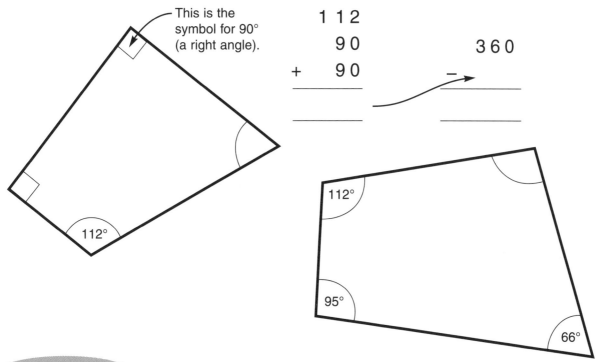

This is the symbol for 90° (a right angle).

```
  1 1 2
    9 0
+   9 0
_____

_____
```

```
  3 6 0
–

_____
```

112°

112°

95°

66°

Quadrilaterals (sides and angles)

Name _____

● Measure the sides of this quadrilateral:

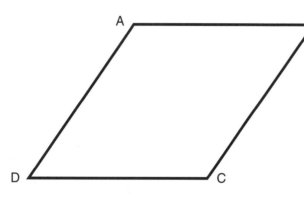

You should find that all the sides are the same length. It is not a square because the vertices are not right angles.

What is the name of the shape? _____

Now measure the angles.

∠ A = _____   ∠ B = _____   ∠ C = _____   ∠ D = _____

∠ A should be equal to ∠ C   ∠ B should be equal to ∠ D

What do the four angles add up to? _____

● Now work on this shape:

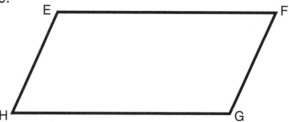

Length of sides: EF = _____ cm   Angles: ∠ E = _____

Length of sides: FG = _____ cm   Angles: ∠ F = _____

Length of sides: GH = _____ cm   Angles: ∠ G = _____

Length of sides: EH = _____ cm   Angles: ∠ H = _____

What is the name of the shape? _____

Notes for teachers

This worksheet provides revision of the facts about quadrilaterals that have been covered on the previous sheets. Encourage the students to measure as accurately as possible with both their rulers and protractors. Be aware that complete accuracy is impossible so they will need to make their best judgements to decide sizes to the nearest whole millimetre or degree.

Andrew Brodie: Supporting Maths 12–13 © A & C Black 2007

Triangles (sides and angles) 1

Name _____

● Measure the sides of this triangle:

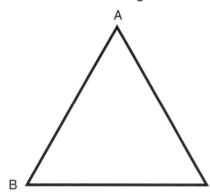

You should find that all the sides are the same length. Because of this it is called an equilateral triangle.

'equi' is from the Latin word for equal.

'lateral' is from the Latin word for side.

Lengths of sides:

AB = _____   AC = _____   BC = _____

Now measure the angles.

∠A = _____   ∠B = _____   ∠C = _____

The angles should all be equal.

What do the angles add up to? _____

● Now work on this triangle:
Lengths of sides:

DE = _____

DF = _____

EF = _____

Angles:

∠D = _____

∠E = _____

∠F = _____

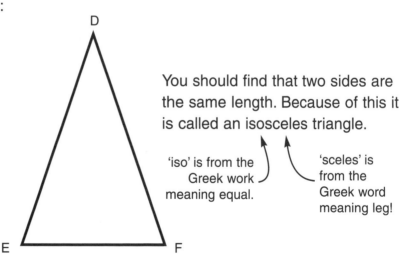

You should find that two sides are the same length. Because of this it is called an isosceles triangle.

'iso' is from the Greek work meaning equal.

'sceles' is from the Greek word meaning leg!

Notes for teachers

Discuss each of the triangles in turn, ensuring that the students recognise which is equilateral and which is isosceles. Use the opportunity to discuss the spellings of these words, encouraging the students to segment them into their phonemes or to split them into syllables. Ask the students to add small markings to the sides of the triangles to show which sides are equal. They can draw a small line on each of the sides of the equilateral and on the two equal sides of the isosceles in the same way that the small lines are drawn on the equal sides of the square on Worksheet 37.

Triangles (sides and angles) 2

Name _____

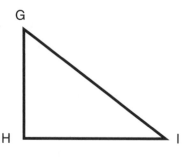

● Measure the angles of this triangle:

∠ G = _____

∠ H = _____

∠ I = _____

Add the three
angles together:

Now just add
∠ G and ∠ I.

+

_____

+

_____

_____

You should have found that angle H is 90°. Angle H is a right angle so this triangle is called a right-angled triangle.

Because angle H is 90° and the fact that 90 + 90 is 180 you should have found that angle G add angle I is 90°.

● Now work on this triangle:
Length of sides:

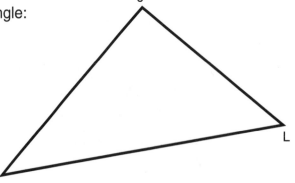

JK = _____

JL = _____

KL = _____

Angles:

∠ J = _____

∠ K = _____

∠ L = _____

You should find
that all the sides
and all the angles
are different.
Because of this it
is called a
'scalene' triangle.

'scalene' is
from the
Greek word
for unequal.

Notes for teachers

Right-angled triangles will become increasingly important in maths as the students move up through the school and learn Pythagoras' theorem and trigonometry. It's important that they recognise a right-angled triangle and that they can see the logic that the other two angles must add up to 90° because 90° + 90° = 180°.

Andrew Brodie: Supporting Maths 12–13 © A & C Black 2007

Areas of squares and rectangles (Discussion sheet)

Name _____

- Look at this square:

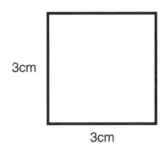

3cm

3cm

The area of a square is the amount of space it covers. This is measured in square centimetres.

You can see that this square covers 9 square centimetres. This is written like this: $9cm^2$

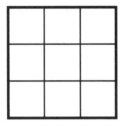

$3cm \times 3cm = 9cm^2$

- Look at this rectangle:

2cm

4cm

This rectangle covers 8 square centimetres.

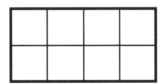

$4cm \times 2cm = 8cm^2$

This rectangle has a length of 3.6cm and a width of 1.4cm

Its area = length x width = $3.6cm \times 1.4cm = 5.04cm^2$

Notes for teachers

Many students confuse area with perimeter. Remind them that area is concerned with the amount of flat space that a shape covers, and is usually measured in square centimetres (or square metres) and that square centimetres can be shown like this: cm^2. You may like to point out the link to square numbers, where the symbol ^{2} is also used: $3^2 = 9$.

Area (squares and rectangles)

Name _____

● Find the areas of these squares and rectangles. Write the answer in each shape.

①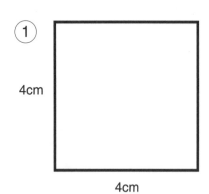
4cm

4cm

②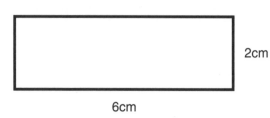
2cm

6cm

③
2.8cm

3.4cm

④
4.2cm

4.2cm

● Find the areas of the shapes below. You will need to measure the lengths of their sides first.

⑤

⑥

Notes for teachers

Point out to the students that they only need to measure one side of a square (if they are sure that the shape is a square) to be able to 'square it' to find the area. With a rectangle, they only need to measure two adjacent sides then multiply to find the area. For questions 3 to 6, the students could use calculators to multiply or they could practise their skills in multiplying decimals as shown on Worksheets 14 and 15.

Perimeter (straight-sided shapes)

Name _____

● Find the perimeters of the shapes below. You will need to measure the lengths of their sides then add them together. Write the answer in each shape.

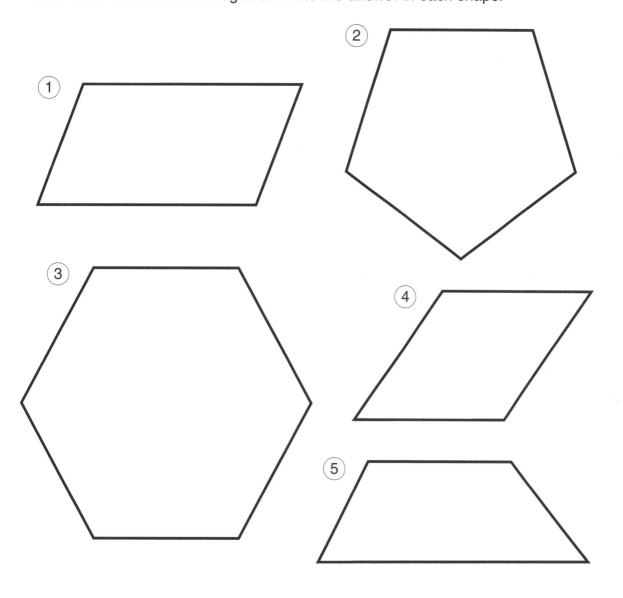

Which was the only shape where you *had to* measure all of the sides? _____

Negative numbers (Discussion sheet)

Name _____

● Sometimes we need to work with negative numbers.

For example, in very cold weather the temperature can fall below zero.

● Look at this example:

At 6pm the temperature in Glasgow is 2° Celsius.

By midnight the temperature has dropped by 4° C.

Q: What is the temperature at midnight?

A: The temperature at midnight is –2°C.

When we talk about temperature we would read this as 'minus two degrees Celsius'. Sometimes though a negative number like this will be called 'negative two'.

● A number line can be very helpful when you work with negative numbers.

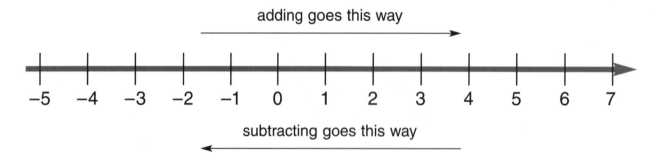

adding goes this way

-5 -4 -3 -2 -1 0 1 2 3 4 5 6 7

subtracting goes this way

Notes for teachers

Students will be familiar with 'minus temperatures' from weather forecasts and this will help with the understanding of the concept for most of them. Discuss the example with them then look carefully at the number line, ensuring that they understand that subtraction works to the left and that addition works to the right. When you feel that they are ready give them Worksheet 46.

Negative numbers (using a number line)

Name _____

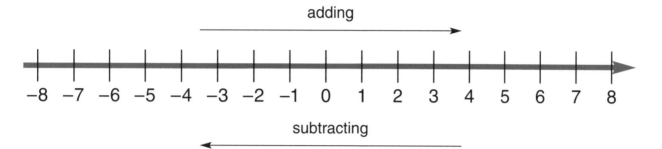

adding

−8 −7 −6 −5 −4 −3 −2 −1 0 1 2 3 4 5 6 7 8

subtracting

● Look at this example:

$$1 - 4 = -3$$

Start at 1 on the number line.

You arrive at −3.

Subtract 4 by moving 4 places to the left.

● Follow this example on the number line:

$$-2 + 6 = 4$$

Adding 6 means moving 6 places to the right.

● Try these:

① −1 + 3 = _____   ② 2 − 5 = _____   ③ −3 + 3 = _____

④ 3 − 7 = _____   ⑤ −7 + 3 = _____   ⑥ −4 + 9 = _____

⑦ 0 − 6 = _____   ⑧ 1 − 5 = _____   ⑨ −8 +16 = _____

⑩ The temperature in Vancouver is −2°C and in San Diego the temperature is 13°C. How much warmer is San Diego than Vancouver? _____

Notes for teachers

Remind the students of how to use the number line, by looking at the examples with them, then help them to answer the questions. Watch how they approach question 10 and encourage them to draw a longer number line to accommodate the question.

Indices

Name _____

● Look:

This is called an index number.
The plural of index is indices.

$$2^2 = 4$$

2^2 means 2 x 2

Similarly

2^3 means 2 x 2 x 2

$$2^3 = \underbrace{2 \times 2}_{4} \times 2 = 8$$

● Find the value of these:

① $3^2 =$ _____

② $4^2 =$ _____

③ $5^2 =$ _____

④ $6^2 =$ _____

⑤ $7^2 =$ _____

⑥ $8^2 =$ _____

⑦ $9^2 =$ _____

⑧ $10^2 =$ _____

⑨ $2^3 =$ _____

⑩ $3^3 =$ _____

● Look:

The index number is sometimes called a 'power'.

$$4^3 =$$

This means 4 to the power of 3.

$$4^3 = \underbrace{4 \times 4}_{16} \times 4 = 64$$

● Try these:

⑪ $5^3 = 5 \times 5 \times 5 =$ _____

⑫ $6^3 =$ _____

Notes for teachers

Students will have seen the use of the index number ^{2} in other aspects of their work: square numbers and area. Point out that the index number shows how many times the number appears in the multiplication. Some students are tempted to interpret 3^2 as 3 x 2 or 2^3 as 2 x 3 and are likely to produce the answer 6 for both of these questions. Look carefully at the examples with them.

Time

Name _____

● Try these:

1. How many days are there in each month?

   January _____   February _____   (February in a leap year) _____

   March _____   April _____   May _____   June _____

   July _____   August _____   September _____

   October _____   November _____   December _____

2. How many hours are there in:

   a) 1 day? _____   b) 2 days? _____   c) 3 days? _____

3. How many minutes are there in:

   a) 1 hour? _____   b) 2 hours? _____   c) $\frac{1}{2}$ hour? _____

   d) $\frac{1}{4}$ hour? _____   e) $\frac{3}{4}$ hour? _____   f) 3 hours? _____

4. How many seconds are there in:

   a) 1 minute? _____   b) 2 minutes? _____   c) 4 minutes? _____

   d) 10 minutes? _____   e) 20 minutes? _____   f) $\frac{1}{2}$ hour? _____

5. How many days are there in 1 year (not a leap year)? _____

6. How many days are there in a leap year? _____

7. Is this year a leap year? _____

8. When is the next leap year? _____

Notes for teachers

This one-off worksheet revises the aspects of time that students are likely to come across in other areas of maths. Help them to answer the questions and to learn the key facts: the days in each month, the number of seconds in a minute, hours in a day, etc. You will probably find that the students know some of these facts really well and are insulted that you are even questioning them on them! However, a surprising number of students have gaps in their knowledge relating to time and some of these gaps may be revealed to you in this work.

Mean, median, mode and range (Discussion sheet)

Name _____

● A group of students had a maths test.

Here are their scores out of 10.

Ahmed	10
Brian	5
Claire	8
Denise	4
Ella	10
Fin	8
George	7
Harry	8
Ingrid	3

The score of 8 occurs three times. The score that appears most has a special name: the *mode*

most → occurring → data entry

● Here are the scores written in order:

3   4   5   7   8   8   8   10   10

This is called the *median* which comes from a Latin word meaning 'middle'.

● The *range* is the biggest value minus the smallest value: $10 - 3 = 7$

● The hardest question to work out is to find the *mean* – it's a really mean question!

Step 1: Add the scores: $10 + 5 + 8 + 4 + 10 + 8 + 7 + 8 + 3 = 63$

Step 2: Divide by the number of scores: $63 \div 9 = 7$

● So for this data the mode is 8, the median is 8, the range is 7 and the mean is 7.

Notes for teachers

The concept of 'mean average' was mentioned on Worksheet 8. This worksheet revises four key pieces of vocabulary used in handling data and provides some clues to remember the words. When you feel that the students are confident with these terms, give them Worksheet 50 which provides further practice.

Data handling (mean, median, mode and range)

Name _____

A group of students had a French test.

Here are their scores out of 20.

Ahmed	18
Brian	14
Claire	17
Denise	12
Ella	15
Fin	17
George	14
Harry	17
Ingrid	20

(1) What was the mode? _____

(2) What was the range? _____

(3) Write the scores in order from lowest to highest.

_____ _____ _____ _____ _____ _____ _____ _____ _____

(4) What was the median score? _____

(5) Add the scores together. Total of scores = _____

(6) Divide the total by the number of scores.

(7) What was the mean? _____

Notes for teachers

This worksheet should be used after the students have examined Worksheet 49. You may like to keep that worksheet available for them to refer to.

Data handling (pie charts) 1

Name _____

⬤ Pie charts are useful for showing information quickly.

Look:

Favourite type of cooked potato chosen by 360 students aged 12–14

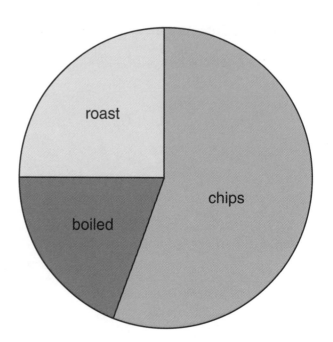

① What is the favourite type of cooked potato of these 360 students? _____

② What is the least popular type? _____

⬤ Because there are 360 degrees made by the radii of a circle you can find the number of people who liked each type of potato. Each person is represented by one degree on the chart. Measure the angles then answer these questions.

③ How many people like chips best? _____

④ How many people like roast potatoes best? _____

⑤ How many people like boiled potatoes best? _____

Notes for teachers

Encourage the students to answer questions 1 and 2 simply by looking at the pie chart. Pie charts are designed for this type of instant recognition of broad statistics that can be found from data. Questions 3, 4 and 5 require much closer examination of the pie chart and students will need to use their skills with protractors to find the answers. The information here is deliberately straightforward as each person is represented by one degree on the chart.

 Andrew Brodie: Supporting Maths 12–13 © A & C Black 2007

Data handling (pie charts) 2

Name _____

Ninety people were asked to name their favourite sport.
The results are shown on this pie chart.

To calculate data follow these steps:

Step 1: Find the total data.
(We've been given that in the question: 90 people.)

Step 2: Measure the angle for each piece of pie.

Step 3: Make a fraction: $\dfrac{\text{angle}}{360°}$

Step 4: Multiply this fraction by the total data (90).

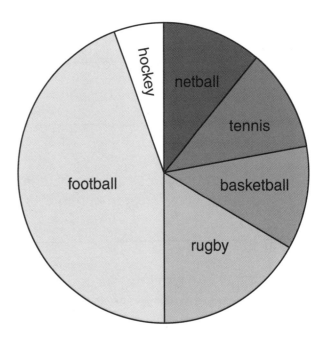

Complete the table to find out the number of people prefer each sport.

	angle	$\dfrac{\text{angle}}{360°}$	$\dfrac{\text{angle}}{360°} \times 90$
football			
netball			
rugby	60°	$\dfrac{60°}{360°}$	15
tennis			
hockey			
basketball			

This column shows the answers we need.

Notes for teachers

This worksheet should be used after Worksheet 51. Again, encourage the students to gain some instant facts from the pie chart such as what was the favourite sport and what was the least favourite, before working through the method shown with them. Make sure that they understand that the table shows the steps involved in solving the question about the actual number of people who prefer each sport and that the last column provides the answers to that question.

Data handling (probability) 1

Name _____

⬤ Some things are *certain*.

Some things are *impossible*.

Some things will probably happen – *likely*.

Some things probably won't happen – *unlikely*.

⬤ We can show these possibilities on a very special number line. The number line is special as it only goes from 0 to 1.

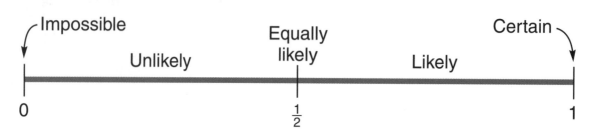

⬤ Write the appropriate word from the number line next to each of the statements below.

(1) Throwing a 7 on an ordinary dice _____

(2) It will rain at some time in the next fortnight. _____

(3) The sun will rise tomorrow. _____

(4) A coin lands 'tails up'. _____

(5) Snow in June in this country _____

Notes for teachers

Look carefully at the number line with the students pointing out that it is a finite line i.e. it does not extend below 0 or above 1 and that impossible is represented by 0 and certain is represented by 1. Discuss the five questions with them. These may cause some healthy debates such as whether it is certain that the sun will rise tomorrow!

Data handling (probability) 2

Name _____

● Excluding jokers, there are 52 cards in a pack of playing cards.
There are four suits:

| diamonds | hearts | clubs | spades |

If you pick a card at random from the pack the chance of it being a diamond is $\frac{13}{52}$, which is the same as $\frac{1}{4}$. The chance of it not being a diamond is $\frac{39}{52}$, which is the same as $\frac{3}{4}$.

$$\frac{13}{52} + \frac{39}{52} = \frac{52}{52} = 1 \qquad\qquad \frac{1}{4} + \frac{3}{4} = \frac{4}{4} = 1$$

Alternative probabilities always add up to 1.

● Try these:

1. Write the fraction that shows the probability of throwing a 6 on an ordinary dice.

   _____

2. Write the fraction that shows the probability of not throwing a 6 on an ordinary dice.

   _____

3. Write the fraction that shows the probability of picking the king of hearts at random from a full pack of cards (no jokers).

   _____

4. Write the fraction that shows the probability of not picking the king of hearts at random from a full pack of cards (no jokers).

   _____

Notes for teachers

This worksheet will be very challenging for many students and they will need considerable help in tackling it. They will need reminding that fractions with the same denominators can simply be added e.g. one quarter of a cake added to three quarters of a cake makes four quarters, which is the same as a whole cake. In working through the questions, point out that because the answer to question 1 is $\frac{1}{6}$, the answer to question 2 must be $\frac{5}{6}$ because $\frac{1}{6} + \frac{5}{6} = 1$. For questions 3 and 4 provide the clue that there is only one king of hearts in a pack of fifty-two cards.

Multiplication tables

1	x	2	=	2
2	x	2	=	4
3	x	2	=	6
4	x	2	=	8
5	x	2	=	10
6	x	2	=	12
7	x	2	=	14
8	x	2	=	16
9	x	2	=	18
10	x	2	=	20

1	x	3	=	3
2	x	3	=	6
3	x	3	=	9
4	x	3	=	12
5	x	3	=	15
6	x	3	=	18
7	x	3	=	21
8	x	3	=	24
9	x	3	=	27
10	x	3	=	30

1	x	4	=	4
2	x	4	=	8
3	x	4	=	12
4	x	4	=	16
5	x	4	=	20
6	x	4	=	24
7	x	4	=	28
8	x	4	=	32
9	x	4	=	36
10	x	4	=	40

1	x	5	=	5
2	x	5	=	10
3	x	5	=	15
4	x	5	=	20
5	x	5	=	25
6	x	5	=	30
7	x	5	=	35
8	x	5	=	40
9	x	5	=	45
10	x	5	=	50

1	x	6	=	6
2	x	6	=	12
3	x	6	=	18
4	x	6	=	24
5	x	6	=	30
6	x	6	=	36
7	x	6	=	42
8	x	6	=	48
9	x	6	=	54
10	x	6	=	60

1	x	7	=	7
2	x	7	=	14
3	x	7	=	21
4	x	7	=	28
5	x	7	=	35
6	x	7	=	42
7	x	7	=	49
8	x	7	=	56
9	x	7	=	63
10	x	7	=	70

1	x	8	=	8
2	x	8	=	16
3	x	8	=	24
4	x	8	=	32
5	x	8	=	40
6	x	8	=	48
7	x	8	=	56
8	x	8	=	64
9	x	8	=	72
10	x	8	=	80

1	x	9	=	9
2	x	9	=	18
3	x	9	=	27
4	x	9	=	36
5	x	9	=	45
6	x	9	=	54
7	x	9	=	63
8	x	9	=	72
9	x	9	=	81
10	x	9	=	90

1	x	10	=	10
2	x	10	=	20
3	x	10	=	30
4	x	10	=	40
5	x	10	=	50
6	x	10	=	60
7	x	10	=	70
8	x	10	=	80
9	x	10	=	90
10	x	10	=	100

Notes for teachers

These tables can be photocopied back to back with the written tables shown on Resource Sheet B. They can be laminated then cut into separate tables so that the child can take them away to practise.

Andrew Brodie: Supporting Maths 12–13 © A & C Black 2007

Multiplication tables in words

One four is four
Two fours are eight
Three fours are twelve
Four fours are sixteen
Five fours are twenty
Six fours are twenty-four
Seven fours are twenty-eight
Eight fours are thirty-two
Nine fours are thirty-six
Ten fours are forty

One three is three
Two threes are six
Three threes are nine
Four threes are twelve
Five threes are fifteen
Six threes are eighteen
Seven threes are twenty-one
Eight threes are twenty-four
Nine threes are twenty-seven
Ten threes are thirty

One two is two
Two twos are four
Three twos are six
Four twos are eight
Five twos are ten
Six twos are twelve
Seven twos are fourteen
Eight twos are sixteen
Nine twos are eighteen
Ten twos are twenty

One seven is seven
Two sevens are fourteen
Three sevens are twenty-one
Four sevens are twenty-eight
Five sevens are thirty-five
Six sevens are forty-two
Seven sevens are forty-nine
Eight sevens are fifty-six
Nine sevens are sixty-three
Ten sevens are seventy

One six is six
Two sixes are twelve
Three sixes are eighteen
Four sixes are twenty-four
Five sixes are thirty
Six sixes are thirty-six
Seven sixes are forty-two
Eight sixes are forty-eight
Nine sixes are fifty-four
Ten sixes are sixty

One five is five
Two fives are ten
Three fives are fifteen
Four fives are twenty
Five fives are twenty-five
Six fives are thirty
Seven fives are thirty-five
Eight fives are forty
Nine fives are forty-five
Ten fives are fifty

One ten is ten
Two tens are twenty
Three tens are thirty
Four tens are forty
Five tens are fifty
Six tens are sixty
Seven tens are seventy
Eight tens are eighty
Nine tens are ninety
Ten tens are a hundred

One nine is nine
Two nines are eighteen
Three nines are twenty-seven
Four nines are thirty-six
Five nines are forty-five
Six nines are fifty-four
Seven nines are sixty-three
Eight nines are seventy-two
Nine nines are eighty-one
Ten nines are ninety

One eight is eight
Two eights are sixteen
Three eights are twenty-four
Four eights are thirty-two
Five eights are forty
Six eights are forty-eight
Seven eights are fifty-six
Eight eights are sixty-four
Nine eights are seventy-two
Ten eights are eighty

Notes for teachers

These tables can be photocopied back to back with the tables shown on Resource sheet A. They can be laminated then cut into separate tables so that the student can take them away to practise.

Mini facts

Multiplication tables

x	1	2	3	4	5	6	7	8	9	10
1	1	2	3	4	5	6	7	8	9	10
2	2	4	6	8	10	12	14	16	18	20
3	3	6	9	12	15	18	21	24	27	30
4	4	8	12	16	20	24	28	32	36	40
5	5	10	15	20	25	30	35	40	45	50
6	6	12	18	24	30	36	42	48	54	60
7	7	14	21	28	35	42	49	56	63	70
8	8	16	24	32	40	48	56	64	72	80
9	9	18	27	36	45	54	63	72	81	90
10	10	20	30	40	50	60	70	80	90	100

Measurement facts

1 kilogram = 1000 grams
(1kg = 1000g)

1 kilometre = 1000 metres
(1km = 1000m)

1 metre = 100 centimetres
(1m = 100cm)

1 metre = 1000 millimetres
(1m = 1000mm)

1 litre = 1000 millilitres
(1l = 1000ml)

Angle facts

The straight line has 180° around this point.

A right angle has 90°.

Two right angles together make a straight line.

a right angle

An acute angle is less than 90°.

an acute angle

An obtuse angle is more than 90° and less than 180°.

an obtuse angle

Shapes

square

rectangle

scalene triangle

equilateral triangle

isosceles triangle

Mini facts

Graphs

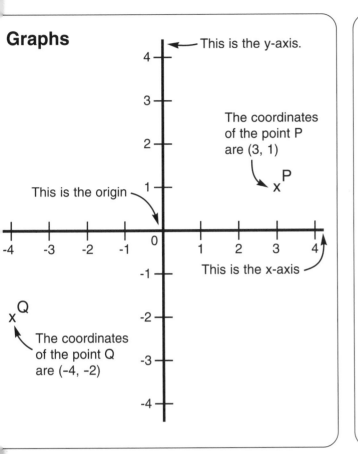

This is the y-axis.

The coordinates of the point P are (3, 1)

This is the origin

This is the x-axis

The coordinates of the point Q are (−4, −2)

More angle facts

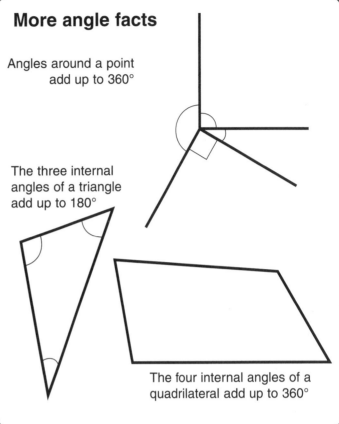

Angles around a point add up to 360°

The three internal angles of a triangle add up to 180°

The four internal angles of a quadrilateral add up to 360°

Months

January	31	June	30
February	28	July	31
(but 29 in a		August	31
leap year)		September	30
March	31	October	31
April	30	November	30
May	31	December	31

Thirty days has September,
April, June and November.
All the rest have thirty-one
Except for February alone
Which has twenty-eight days clear
And twenty-nine in each leap year.

Shapes

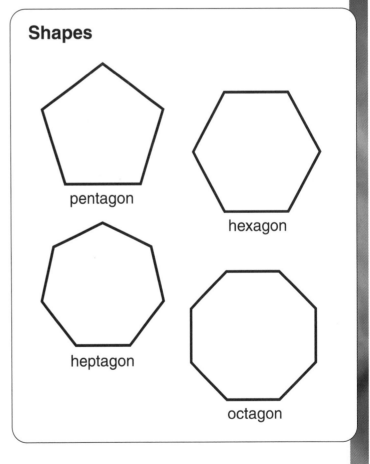

pentagon

hexagon

heptagon

octagon

Mini facts

Circle facts

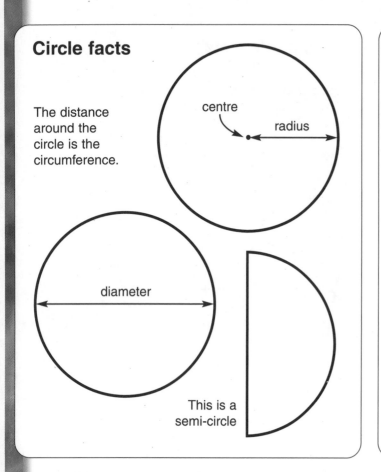

The distance around the circle is the circumference.

centre

radius

diameter

This is a semi-circle

Square numbers

$1^2 = 1$

$2^2 = 4$

$3^2 = 9$

$4^2 = 16$

$5^2 = 25$

$6^2 = 36$

$7^2 = 49$

$8^2 = 64$

$9^2 = 81$

$10^2 = 100$

$11^2 = 121$

$12^2 = 144$

Cube numbers

$2^3 = 2 \times 2 \times 2 = 8$

$3^3 = 3 \times 3 \times 3 = 27$

Fractions, decimals and percentages

$\frac{1}{2} = 0.5 = 50\%$

$\frac{1}{4} = 0.25 = 25\%$

$\frac{3}{4} = 0.75 = 75\%$

$\frac{1}{10} = 0.1 = 10\%$

$\frac{2}{10} = 0.2 = 20\%$

$\frac{1}{3} = 0.333333$ (This would go on forever so we write 0.3̇ instead.)

$\frac{2}{3} = 0.666666$ (This would go on forever so we write 0.6̇ instead.)

Shape facts

parallelogram

rhombus

kite

trapezium

Andrew Brodie: Supporting Maths 12–13 © A & C Black 2007